MY PERSONAL WORD BOOK

Published by
Prim-Ed Publishing

Alphabetical Themes

- **A**nimals
- **B**each
- **C**olour
- **D**inosaurs
- **E**arth
- **F**arm
- **G**ames
- **H**ospital
- **I**nsects
- **J**ungle
- **K**itchen
- **L**ibrary
- **M**oney
- **N**oises
- **O**cean
- **P**ark
- **Q**ueen
- **R**estaurant
- **S**pace
- **T**ransport
- **U**niforms
- **V**egetables
- **W**eather
- **X**mas
- **Y**oung
- **Z**oo

Extra Themes

Prim-Ed Publishing

How to Use My Personal Word Book

• Here is what you will find inside your word book.

Print your letters in this box.

Alphabet Words
Lists of important words for each letter of the alphabet.

Animals

bird
camel
cat
dog
elephant
fish
frog
giraffe
goat

horse
leopard
lion
mouse
rabbit
sheep
snake
turtle
zebra

My 'Aa' words

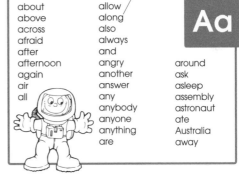

about
above
across
afraid
after
afternoon
again
air
all

allow
along
also
always
and
angry
another
answer
any
anybody
anyone
anything
are

around
ask
asleep
assembly
astronaut
ate
Australia
away

My 'Aa' words

Theme Words
A set of topic words for each letter of the alphabet.

My 'Aa' Words
Lines to print your own interesting alphabet words.

Animals

bird
camel
cat
dog
elephant
fish
frog
giraffe
goat

horse
leopard
lion
mouse
rabbit
sheep
snake
turtle
zebra

My 'Aa' words

Prim-Ed Publishing

Aa

about
above
across
afraid
after
afternoon
again
air
all

allow
along
also
always
am
an
and
angry
another
answer
any
anybody
anyone
anything

are
around
as
ask
asleep
assembly
astronaut
at
ate
away

My 'Aa' words

Beach

bucket
hat
jetty
kiosk
lifeguard
paddle
sand
sandcastle
seaweed

shell
shorts
spade
splash
sunscreen
surfboard
swim
towel
umbrella

My 'Bb' words

_____   _____   _____

_____   _____   _____

_____   _____   _____

_____   _____   _____

_____   _____   _____

Prim-Ed Publishing

baby
back
bad
ball
balloon
bang
bath
be
beautiful
because

bed
been
before
began
believe
belong
best
better
big
bike
birthday
body
book
both

boy
breakfast
bring
broken
brother
build
busy
but
buy
by

My 'Bb' words

_____   _____

_____   _____   _____

_____   _____   _____

_____   _____   _____

_____   _____   _____

_____   _____   _____

Colour

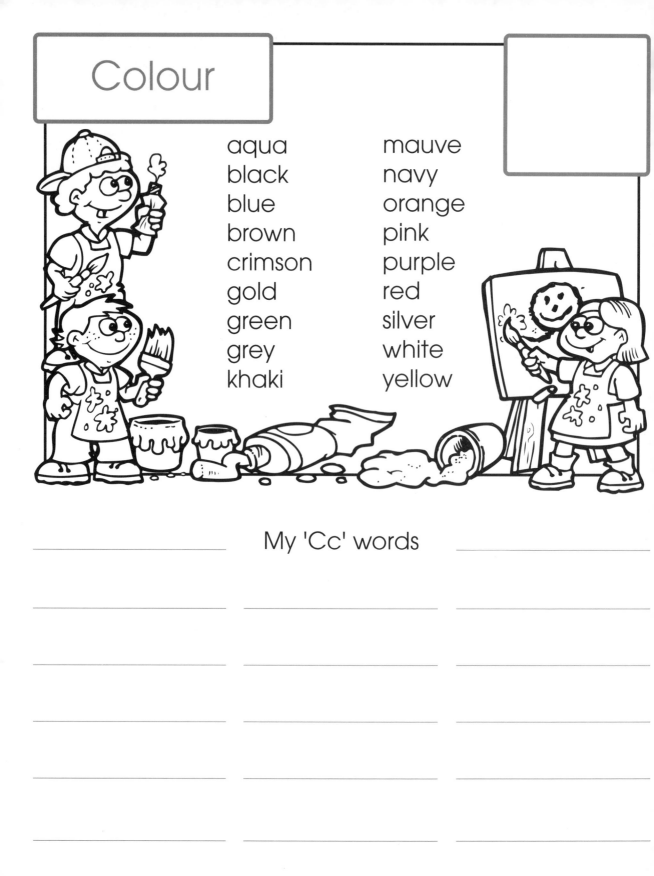

aqua
black
blue
brown
crimson
gold
green
grey
khaki

mauve
navy
orange
pink
purple
red
silver
white
yellow

My 'Cc' words

Prim-Ed Publishing

cake	caught	
call	children	**Cc**
came	Christmas	
can	city	
can't	classroom	
car	clean	come
carry	climb	could
catch	clock	couldn't
	close	count
	clothes	country
	clown	cried
	coin	cross
	cold	cry
	colour	cut

My 'Cc' words

_____ _____ _____

_____ _____ _____

_____ _____ _____

_____ _____ _____

_____ _____ _____

Dinosaurs

carnivore
claws
diplodocus
extinct
footprint
fossil
herbivore
horn
iguanodon

museum
prehistoric
pterodactyl
reptile
scales
stegosaurus
teeth
triceratops
tyrannosaurus rex

My 'Dd' words

Prim-Ed Publishing

Dd

dangerous
dark
date
day
dead
dear
deep
dentist

did
didn't
different
dig
dirty
divide
do
doctor (Dr)
does
doesn't
doing
dollar
done
don't

door
down
draw
dream
drink
drive
drop
dry
during

My 'Dd' words

Earth

air
cliff
continent
island
lake
land
mountain
North Pole
river

rock
sand
sea
soil
South Pole
stream
valley
volcano
water

My 'Ee' words

Prim-Ed Publishing

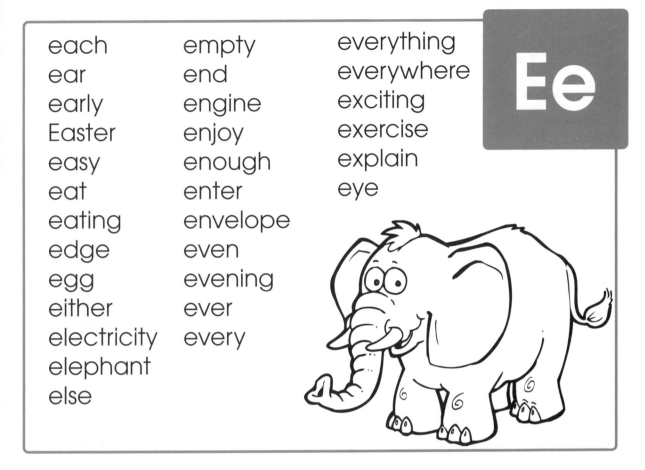

each
ear
early
Easter
easy
eat
eating
edge
egg
either
electricity
elephant
else

empty
end
engine
enjoy
enough
enter
envelope
even
evening
ever
every

everything
everywhere
exciting
exercise
explain
eye

Ee

My 'Ee' words

Farm

barn
cattle
chicken
cow
crop
farmer
field

goat
harvester
herd
horse
lamb
paddock
plough
shearer

sheep
tractor
wheat
wool

My 'Ff' words

_____   _____   _____

_____   _____   _____

_____   _____   _____

_____   _____   _____

_____   _____   _____

_____   _____   _____

Prim-Ed Publishing

Ff

face
fall
family
far
fast
favourite
feel
few

fight
find
finger
finish
fire
first
fish
floor
fly
food
foot
for
forgot
found

Friday
friend
frightened
from
front
fruit
full
funny

My 'Ff' words

_____ _____ _____

Games

ball
basketball
bat
chess
cricket
crossword
dice
football
hockey

hopscotch
jigsaw
marbles
netball
racquet
rugby
soccer
tennis
yoyo

My 'Gg' words

_____   _____   _____

_____   _____   _____

_____   _____   _____

_____   _____   _____

_____   _____   _____

_____   _____   _____

Prim-Ed Publishing

game	getting	
garden	giant	**Gg**
gardener	giggle	
gate	girl	
gave	give	got
gentle	glad	grab
get	glass	gram
	glue	grape
	go	grass
	goes	great
	going	ground
	gone	group
	good	grow
	goodbye	guess

My 'Gg' words

_____   _____

_____   _____   _____

_____   _____   _____

_____   _____   _____

_____   _____   _____

_____   _____   _____

Hospital

accident
ambulance
anaesthetic
bandage
doctor
emergency
medicine
needle
nurse

operation
patient
prescription
sister
splint
stethoscope
thermometer
ward
wheelchair

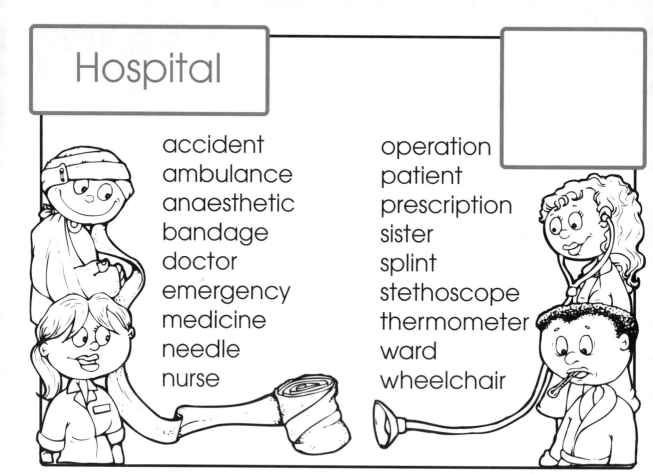

My 'Hh' words

_____   _____   _____

_____   _____   _____

_____   _____   _____

_____   _____   _____

_____   _____   _____

Prim-Ed Publishing

had
hair
half
happy
hard
has
hasn't
have

haven't
having
he
heard
heavy
helicopter
hello
help
her
here
hide
high
him
his

hold
home
hope
hour
house
how
hungry
hurry
hurt

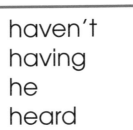

My 'Hh' words

Insects

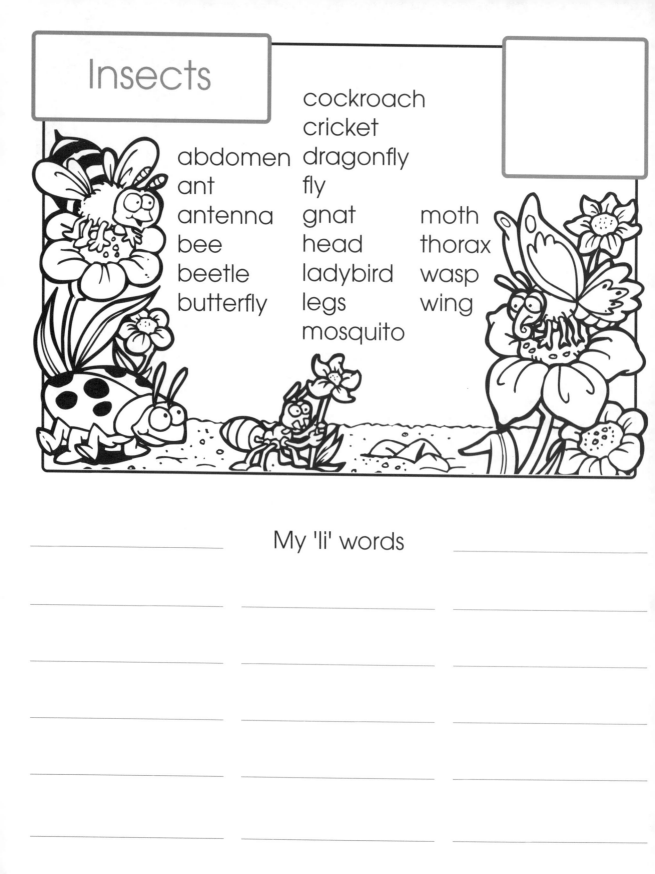

abdomen
ant
antenna
bee
beetle
butterfly

cockroach
cricket
dragonfly
fly
gnat
head
ladybird
legs
mosquito

moth
thorax
wasp
wing

My 'li' words

Prim-Ed Publishing

I
ice
ice-cream
idea
if
ill
I'll
I'm

important
in
inside
instead
instruction
interesting
into

invitation
invite
iron
is
island
isn't
it
itchy
it's

My 'Ii' words

Jungle

anaconda
ape
baboon
chimpanzee
creeper
fern
gibbon
gorilla
green

leopard
monkey
python
rain
rainforest
swamp
tiger
tropical
vine

My 'Jj' words

Prim-Ed Publishing

Jj

jam
jar
jaw
jeans
jelly
jellyfish
jet
jetty

jewellery
jigsaw
job
jog
join
joke
journey

jug
juice
jump
jumper
junk
just

My 'Jj' words

_____

_____

_____

_____

_____

_____

_____

_____

_____

_____

_____

_____

_____

_____

_____

Kitchen

bowl
cook
dishwasher
fork
freezer
frying pan
ingredients
knife
ladle

oven
plate
recipe
refrigerator
saucepan
sink
spatula
spoon
toaster

My 'Kk' words

Prim-Ed Publishing

kangaroo
keep
kept
key
kick
kilogram
kilometre
kind
king

kiss
kite
kitten
knee

knew
knife
knit
knitting
knock
knot
know
koala

My 'Kk' words

Library

atlas
author
book
browse
character
contents
cover
dictionary
fiction

illustrator
index
librarian
non-fiction
reference
shelf
spine
story
title

My 'Ll' words

Prim-Ed Publishing

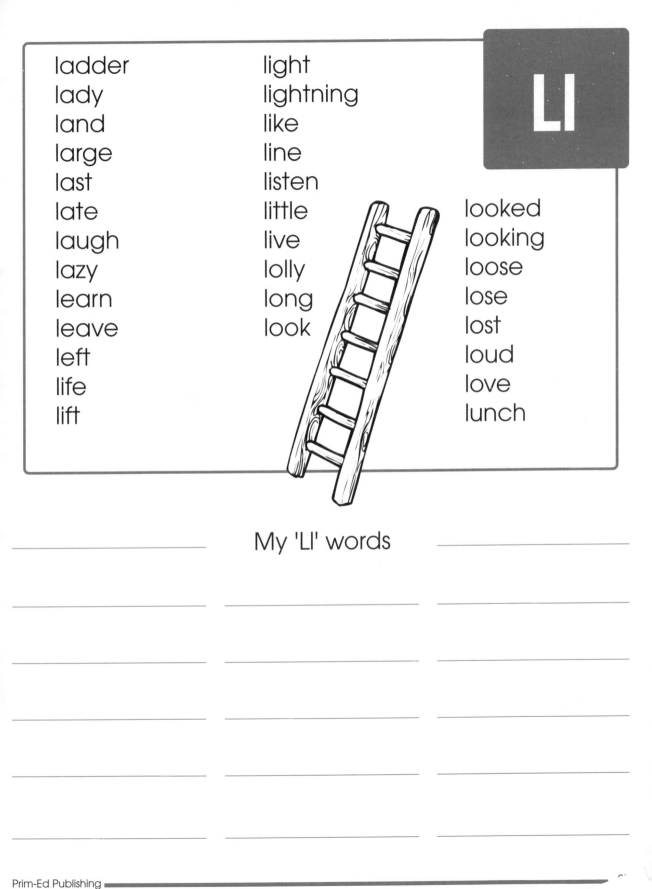

ladder	light	
lady	lightning	
land	like	
large	line	
last	listen	
late	little	looked
laugh	live	looking
lazy	lolly	loose
learn	long	lose
leave	look	lost
left		loud
life		love
lift		lunch

Ll

My 'Ll' words

Money

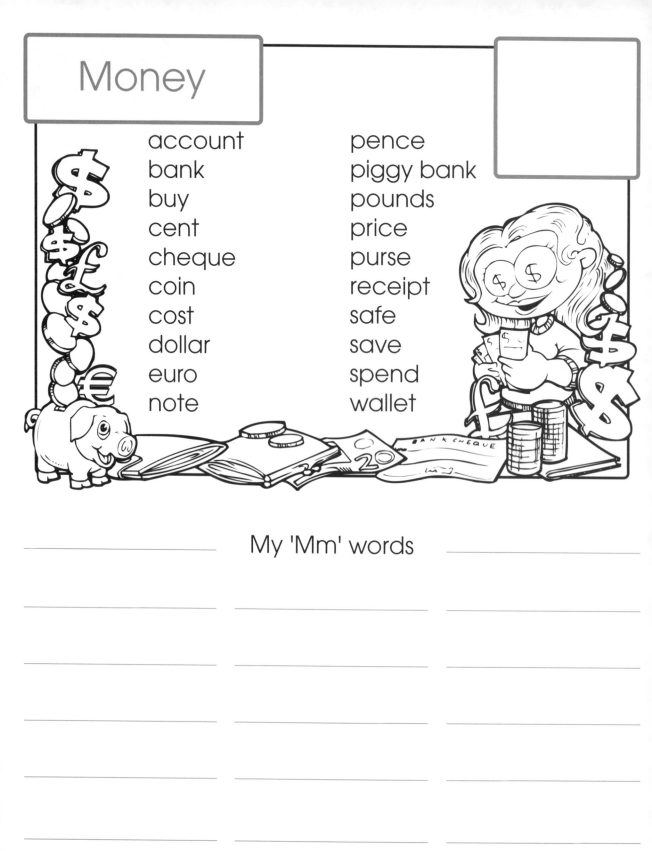

account
bank
buy
cent
cheque
coin
cost
dollar
euro
note

pence
piggy bank
pounds
price
purse
receipt
safe
save
spend
wallet

My 'Mm' words

Prim-Ed Publishing

Mm

made
magic
make
making
man
many
may
me

measure
mess
metres
middle
might
milk
mind
mine
minute
mistake
Monday
monkey
month
moon

more
morning
most
move
much
music
must
my
myself

My 'Mm' words

Noises

baa
bang
bark
buzz
creak
croak
cry
echo
hoot

miaow
moo
neigh
oink
ouch
quack
roar
scream
shout

My 'Nn' words

Prim-Ed Publishing

Nn

nail
name
narrow
naughty

near
nearly
neat
need
neighbour
nest
never
new
news
newspaper
next
nice
night
no

nobody
noise
none
nose
not
note
nothing
now
number
nurse

My 'Nn' words

Ocean

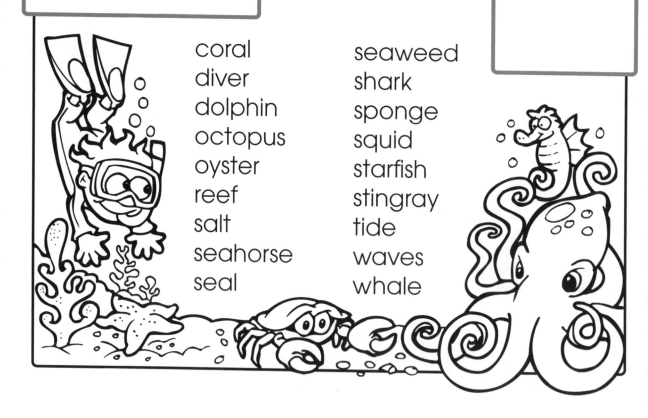

coral
diver
dolphin
octopus
oyster
reef
salt
seahorse
seal

seaweed
shark
sponge
squid
starfish
stingray
tide
waves
whale

My 'Oo' words

Prim-Ed Publishing

o'clock
octopus
odd
of
off

often
oil
old
on
once
one
only
open
opened
opening
opposite
or
orange
orchestra

other
our
ourselves
out
outside
oven
over
owl
own

Oo

My 'Oo' words

Park

bench
duck
flower
footpath
fountain
garden
grass
lake
lawn

picnic
playground
pond
sandpit
seat
shade
slide
swing
tree

My 'Pp' words

Prim-Ed Publishing

Pp

pack	person	
page	pet	
pain	picture	
paint	piece	
paper	place	
party	plate	pretty
past	play	prize
pencil	played	promise
people	playing	pull
	please	push
	police	put
	pool	putting
	present	pyjamas
	pretend	

My 'Pp' words

_____ _____ _____

_____ _____ _____

_____ _____ _____

_____ _____ _____

_____ _____ _____

_____ _____ _____

Queen

carriage
castle
ceremony
crown
curtsy
duchess
duke
king
moat

parade
prince
princess
regal
royal
sword
tiara
tower
turret

My 'Qq' words

Prim-Ed Publishing

Qq

quack
quarter
queer
question
quick
quickly
quiet
quietly
quilt
quite
quiz

My 'Qq' words

Restaurant

bill
chef
dessert
eat
entree
lasagne
main course
manners
menu

noodles
order
pizza
rice
serve
spaghetti
steak
taco
waiter

My 'Rr' words

Prim-Ed Publishing

Rr

race
rain
rainbow
raincoat
ran
reach
read
ready
real

really
reason
remember
reply
rest
rich
ride
riding
right
road
rocket
roll
roof

room
rough
round
row
rubber
ruler
run
running

My 'Rr' words

Space

alien
astronaut
Earth
Jupiter
Mars
Mercury
moon
Neptune
orbit

planet
Pluto
rocket
Saturn
space shuttle
star
sun
Uranus
Venus

My 'Ss' words

Prim-Ed Publishing

Ss

sad
safe
said
same
Saturday
saw
says
scared
school
second
see
seen
share
she

shoe
shop
should
shout
show
shut
sleep
slow
small
so
some
someone

something
sometimes
soon
story
street
suddenly
Sunday
surprise
swim

My 'Ss' words

Transport

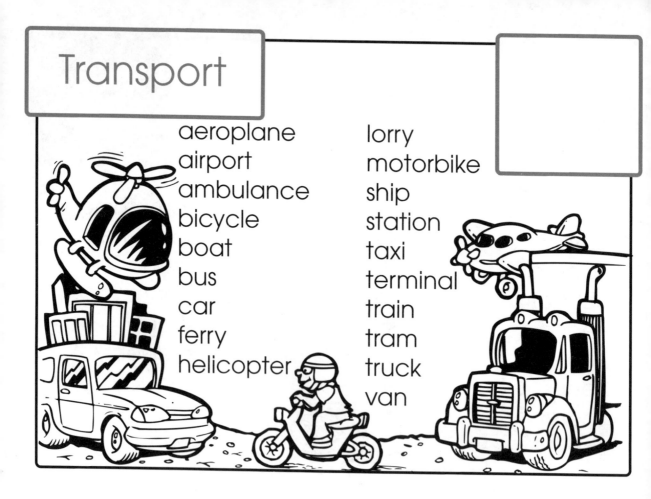

aeroplane
airport
ambulance
bicycle
boat
bus
car
ferry
helicopter

lorry
motorbike
ship
station
taxi
terminal
train
tram
truck
van

My 'Tt' words

Prim-Ed Publishing

Tt

take
talk
teacher
telephone
television
than
thank
that
the
their
them
then
there

these
they
thing
this
thought
threw
through
Thursday
time
tired
to
today
together
told

tomorrow
tonight
too
took
toy
tree
tried
try
Tuesday
turn

My 'Tt' words

Uniforms

badge
belt
blazer
boots
braid
button
cap

cape
collar
crest
gown
hat
helmet
jacket

lapel
pocket
tie
vest

My 'Uu' words

Prim-Ed Publishing

Uu

ugly
umbrella
umpire
uncle
under

underneath
understand
undo
undone
unkind
unless
unlucky
untidy
until

up
upon
upset
upside-down
upstairs
us
use
used
useful

My 'Uu' words

Vegetables

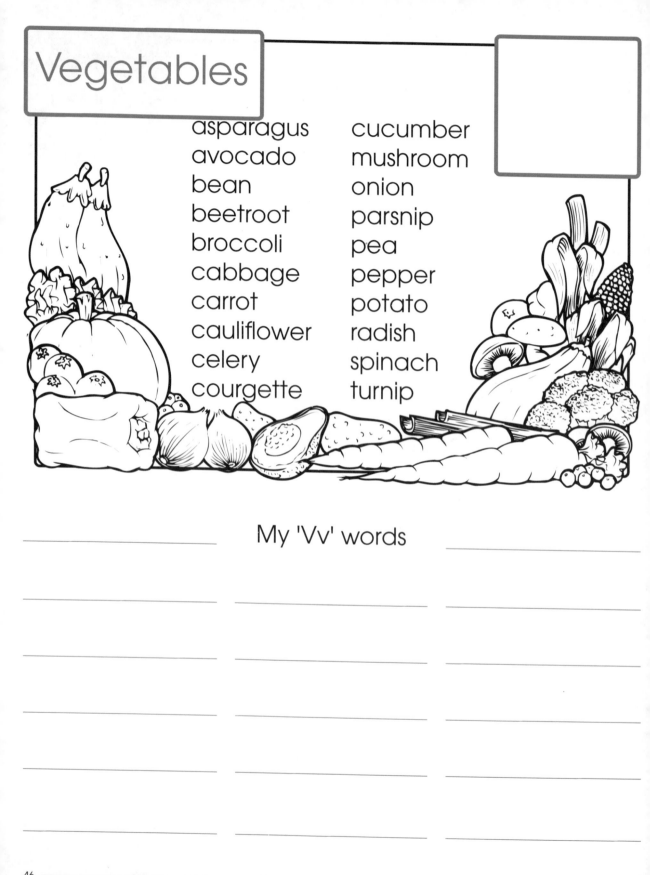

asparagus
avocado
bean
beetroot
broccoli
cabbage
carrot
cauliflower
celery
courgette

cucumber
mushroom
onion
parsnip
pea
pepper
potato
radish
spinach
turnip

My 'Vv' words

Prim-Ed Publishing

van
vanish
vase
vehicle

very
vet
video
videotape

violin
virus
visit
voice
volcano
vote

My 'Vv' words

_____

_____

_____

Weather

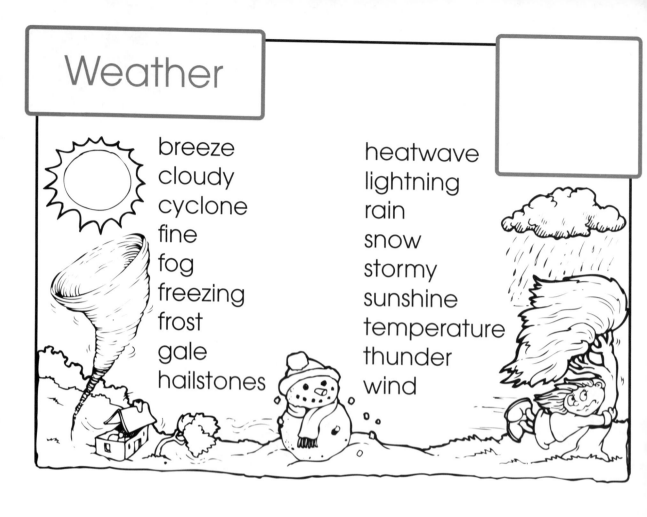

breeze
cloudy
cyclone
fine
fog
freezing
frost
gale
hailstones

heatwave
lightning
rain
snow
stormy
sunshine
temperature
thunder
wind

My 'Ww' words

Prim-Ed Publishing

Ww

walk	went	
want	were	
warm	what	
was	when	
wasn't	where	wish
watch	which	with
water	who	without
way	whole	won
we	why	work
wear	will	world
Wednesday	window	would
week		wouldn't
weekend		write
weigh		wrong

My 'Ww' words

Xmas

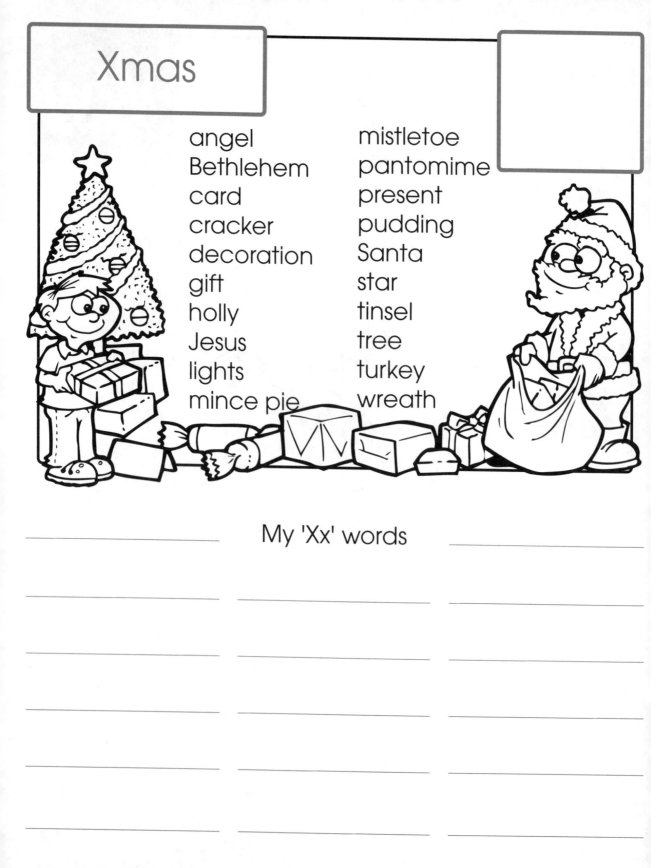

angel
Bethlehem
card
cracker
decoration
gift
holly
Jesus
lights
mince pie

mistletoe
pantomime
present
pudding
Santa
star
tinsel
tree
turkey
wreath

My 'Xx' words

Prim-Ed Publishing

X-ray
xylophone

Xx

My 'Xx' words

Young

baby
calf
chick
child
cub
cygnet
duckling
eaglet
foal

gosling
joey
kid
kitten
lamb
nestling
piglet
puppy
tadpole

My 'Yy' words

Prim-Ed Publishing

Yy

yacht
yard
yawn
year
yell
yelled
yelling
yellow
yes
yesterday
yet
yoghurt

yoke
you
young
younger

youngest
your
you're
yours
yourself
youth
yoyo

My 'Yy' words

Zoo

bear
cage
camel
chimpanzee
crocodile
elephant
giraffe
koala
lion

monkey
nocturnal
orang-outang
polar bear
snake
tiger
tortoise
zebra
zoo keeper

My 'Zz' words

Prim-Ed Publishing

zap
zebra
zebra crossing
zero
zest
zigzag
zinc
zip
zippy
zircon

zither
zone
zoo
zoom

Zz

My 'Zz' words

People in My Family

aunt	daughter	grandmother	niece
baby	father	mother	sister
brother	grandad	mum	son
cousin	grandfather	nanna	uncle
dad	grandma	nephew	

People in My Community

architect	farmer		painter
baker	firefighter		pilot
bank teller	florist		plumber
bricklayer	gardener		police officer
builder	greengrocer		scientist
butcher		hairdresser	secretary
carpenter		librarian	shop assistant
chemist		mechanic	student
dentist		miner	teacher
doctor		newsagent	truck driver
electrician		nurse	veterinarian

Prim-Ed Publishing

Feelings

angry
annoyed
bored
cheerful
content
cross
delighted
disappointed
dislike
excited
friendly

frightened
glad
happy
helpful
hopeful
interested
loving
lucky
miserable
nervous

pleased
proud
puzzled
sad
scared
sleepy
surprised
tearful
tired
upset
worried

What I Can Do

balance
carry
catch
climb
crawl
creep
cry
cut
dance
draw
dress
drink
eat
exercise
glue

help
hide
hop
jump
laugh
leap
learn
listen
look
paint
play
pretend
print
read
run
shout

sing
sit
skip
sleep
smile
swim
talk
think
try
wait
wash
watch
whisper
work
write

Prim-Ed Publishing

At School

bell
blackboard
break
car park
chair
chalk
classroom
computer
crayons
desk
dictionary
drawing pins
eraser
exercise book
glue
homework
library
lunch box
lunchtime
office
pad

paper
pen
pencil
pencil case
playground
playtime
Principal
ruck sack
ruler
school bag
scissors
scrapbook
staff room

string
tape
teacher
television
video

Animals

ant
bear
beaver
butterfly
cow
crocodile
dolphin
duck
emu
gibbon
hog
iguana
kangaroo

koala
ostrich
parrot
pig
rat
seal
sheep
tiger

walrus
whale

Prim-Ed Publishing

Words that Sound the Same

ate – eight
be – bee
bean – been
blew – blue
buy – by

eye – I
fair – fare
for – four
hear – here
hour – our
knew – new
know – no
meat – meet
oar – or
one – won
pair – pear

raw – roar
red – read
road – rode
sail – sale
saw – sore
sea – see
sew – so
there – their
threw – through
to – too – two
weak – week

Contractions

aren't – are not
can't – can not
couldn't – could not
didn't – did not
doesn't – does not
don't – do not
hasn't – has not
haven't – have not
I'll – I will
I'm – I am

isn't – is not
I've – I have
they'll – they will
they're – they are
they've – they have
wasn't – was not
we'll – we will
we're – we are
won't – will not
wouldn't – would not

Seasons

Summer

Autumn

Winter

Spring

Days of the Week

Sunday
Monday
Tuesday
Wednesday
Thursday
Friday
Saturday

Months of the Year

January
February
March
April
May
June
July
August
September
October
November
December

Prim-Ed Publishin

Numbers

1	one	40	forty
2	two	50	fifty
3	three	60	sixty
4	four	70	seventy
5	five	80	eighty
6	six	90	ninety
7	seven	100	one hundred
8	eight	200	two hundred
9	nine	300	three hundred
10	ten	400	four hundred
11	eleven	500	five hundred
12	twelve	600	six hundred
13	thirteen	700	seven hundred
14	fourteen	800	eight hundred
15	fifteen	900	nine hundred
16	sixteen	1 000	one thousand
17	seventeen	5 000	five thousand
18	eighteen	10 000	ten thousand
19	nineteen	1 000 000	one million
20	twenty		
30	thirty		

Shapes

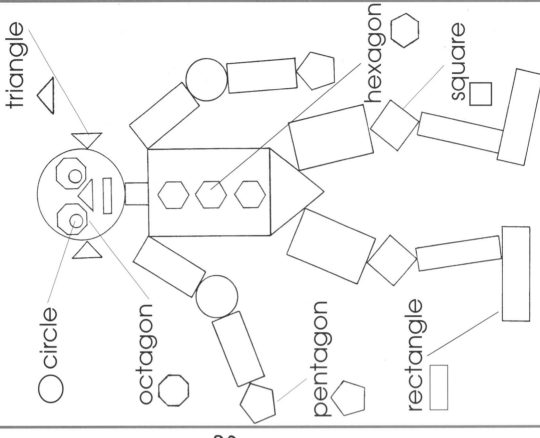

triangle

hexagon

square

circle

octagon

pentagon

rectangle

Parts of the Body

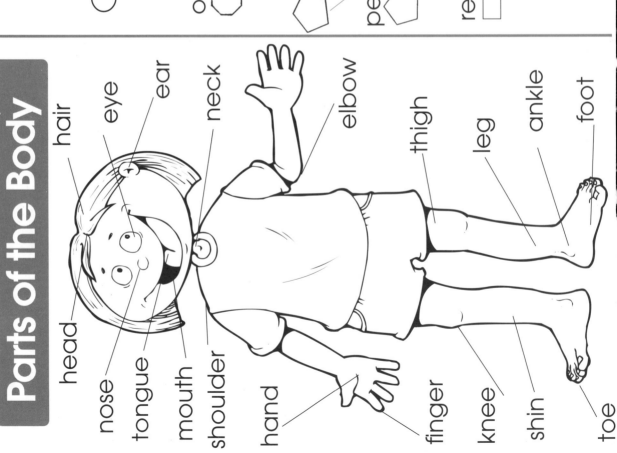

hair

eye

ear

neck

elbow

thigh

leg

ankle

foot

head

nose

tongue

mouth

shoulder

hand

finger

knee

shin

toe